Supporting Literacy

FOR AGES 10–11

CW01084284

Andrew Brodie

Introduction

Supporting Literacy is aimed at all those who work with children who have been identified as needing 'additional' or 'different' literacy support. It can be used by anyone working with children who fall into this category, whether you are a teacher, classroom assistant or parent.

Typically the ten to eleven year-old children for whom the book is intended will be working at the levels expected of Year 4 or Year 5 children or may simply need extra help in tackling the standard of work expected of Year 6. Their difficulties may be short term, and overcome with extra practice and support on a one to one or small group basis, or they may be long term where such support enables them to make progress but at a level behind their peer group. The activities in this book provide exactly what these children need – plenty of repetition and practice of basic skills, often covering the same ground but in a slightly different way. For this reason, you might decide to use the worksheets in a different order or just select the sheets that are suitable for the child or group of children you are working with. All the activities can be used on their own or alongside other literacy schemes that are already established within your school.

The worksheets are simple and self-explanatory and the instruction text is deliberately kept to a minimum to make the pages easy for adults to use and less daunting for children to follow. At the bottom of each page 'Notes for teachers' summarise the purpose of the activity and the learning target that is being addressed. Suggestions for additional activities are included if appropriate.

Most of the worksheets are based upon the National Literacy Strategy (NLS) objectives but some, where possible and relevant, are linked to other aspects of the curriculum. Through many years of experience of working with special needs children, the authors have been able to select the areas that these children find most difficult and provide useful activities that specifically address these stumbling blocks. Accordingly, and as set out below, most of the worksheets are centred around the word level strand of the Literacy Strategy.

The main targets addressed in this book are:

- Reading and spelling the NLS medium frequency words for Years 4 and 5
- Using a dictionary, spell checker or word bank to support written work
- Using alphabetical order by looking at the third and fourth letters of the words where necessary
- Using commas in lists and sentences
- Using capital letters at the start of sentences and for names, headings, days, months, the start of direct speech
- Using full stops at the end of sentences
- Using speech marks, question marks, exclamation marks
- Using the terms noun, verb, adjective, adverb
- Understand that tense refers to time and to use tenses appropriately
- Recognising prefixes and suffixes
- Recognising compound words
- Working effectively with regular and irregular plurals of words
- Learning some of the vocabulary associated with topics in other curriculum areas that will be covered in Year 6

However you decide to use these sheets and in whatever context, it is worth remembering that children generally achieve the greatest success in an atmosphere of support and encouragement. Praise from a caring adult can be the best reward for children's efforts. The worksheets and activities in this book will provide many opportunities for children to enjoy their successes. The resulting increase in self-esteem will make a difference to their school work and other areas of school life too.

Andrew Brodie: Supporting Literacy © A & C Black Publishers Ltd. 2006

Individual record sheet

Name:

Worksheet	Teaching and learning objective	Target achieved	Needs more practice
1–2	to put words into alphabetical order using the 3rd or 4th letters		
3–4	to use the prefix **al**		
5–6	to use the regular verb ending **ed**		
7–8	to use/spell irregular tense changes		
9–10	to spell words ending ight		
11–12	to read and spell words ending in tion		
13–14	to read and spell words ending in sion		
15–16	to use and spell the word ending ful		
17–18	to read and spell the word ending ious		
19–20	to read and spell words ending in ive		
21–22	to read and spell words ending in ough		
23–24	to recognise compound words and to use them as an aid to spelling		
25–26	to understand the term 'adverb'		
27–28	to understand the term 'adjective'		
29–30	to use the terms singular and plural, and to begin to investigate how spellings may change when a noun becomes a plural		
31–34	to write sentences demarcated by appropriate use of capital letters and full stops; to make use of a dictionary card to assist with spelling		
35	to read and spell words associated with history and Geography covered in Year 6		
36	to read and spell words associated with Science covered in Year 6		
37–41	to read and spell words from the medium frequency list; to arrange words in alphabetical order		

Record and Review

Name: _____   Date of birth: _____

Teacher: _____   Class: _____

Support assistant: _____

Code of Practice stage: _____   Date targets set: _____

Target

1 _____

2 _____

3 _____

4 _____

Review

Target

1 _____

_____

_____   Target achieved? ☐ Date: _____

2 _____

_____

_____   Target achieved? ☐ Date: _____

3 _____

_____

_____   Target achieved? ☐ Date: _____

4 _____

_____

_____   Target achieved? ☐ Date: _____

Andrew Brodie: Supporting Literacy © A & C Black Publishers Ltd. 2006

Content of the worksheets

The activities in this book are based on 'tracking back' in the Literacy Framework to provide appropriate materials for Year 6 pupils who need extra attention and support. Each worksheet features a main activity and most also include a subsidiary activity – the garden path.

The garden path, which appears in a variety of different guises, contains NLS high frequency words for reading practice. Each path introduces a new word and provides practice of several words that have appeared on previous paths. As a child reads each word successfully they can colour the appropriate shape on the path. This can also serve as a useful tool for recording a child's progress over a series of lessons.

Worksheets 1–2 provide practice in sorting words into alphabetical order using the third or fourth letters.

Worksheets 3–4 feature the use of the prefix al, while worksheets 5-6 consider the use of the regular verb ending ed.

Worksheets 7–8 deal with some of the irregular tense changes.

Worksheets 9–22 all give practice in reading particular word endings, including ight, tion, sion, ful, ious, ive and ough.

Worksheets 23–24 consider compound words.

Worksheets 25–30 provide revision of the terms adverb, adjective, singular and plural..

Worksheets 31–34 consist of dictation exercises that offer excellent practice of writing well-punctuated sentences.

Worksheets 35–36 introduce some of the vocabulary associated with topics likely to be covered in Year 6 history, geography and science lessons.

Worksheets 37–41 feature practice in reading and spelling words from the medium frequency list.

Pages 48–55 contain a complete reading test to ascertain pupils' knowledge of the medium frequency words specified for Years 4 and 5 in the National Literacy Strategy. Teachers are able to gain a percentage score for each pupil. The test can be repeated after several months to check pupils' progress.

Pages 57–60 can be used to create a personal dictionary card for each pupil. Much use of this can be made when tackling exercises from the book but also within class lessons. This provides a valuable resource for children of all abilities.

The final section of the book (**pages 61–64**) can be photocopied to create record sheets to show pupils' progress in learning to read and to spell the medium frequency words.

Name: _____

Date: _____

a b c d e f g h i j k l m n o p q r s t u v w x y z

This page from a dictionary is in the wrong order.
Cut out the strips. Sort them into alphabetical order.
Stick the correctly arranged strips into your book.

bride	a woman on the day of her wedding
bread	a type of food
breeze	a light wind
bright	shiny
bridge	a crossing over a river, road or railway
break	to smash something

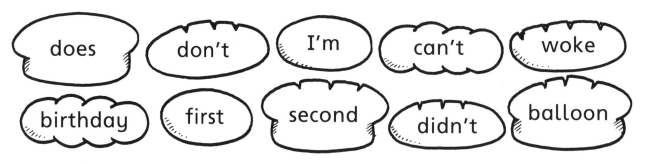

Notes for teachers

Target: To put words into alphabetical order using the 3rd or 4th letters

You may need to remind pupils how to put words into alphabetical order by giving them a list of words to arrange according to the first letter of each, e.g. jigsaw, elephant, school, banana. If they are confident with this activity, try words where the first letter is the same: dog, dinner, dragonfly, date. Then read the instructions for this activity with them and ensure they understand what to do, as this is an important part of any written activity. As an extension activity pupils could arrange the names of their classmates in alphabetical order. Explain that it is usual to sort names by surname rather than by first name.

     Andrew Brodie: Supporting Literacy © A & C Black Publishers Ltd. 2006

a b c d e f g h i j k l m n o p q r s t u v w x y z

Put the words from the shell in alphabetical order.

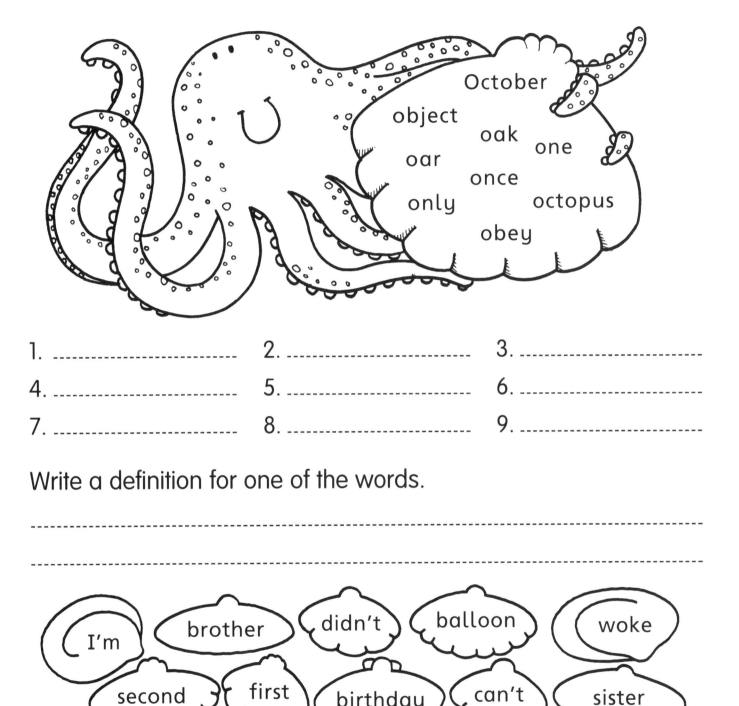

October

object

oak

oar

one

once

only

octopus

obey

1. _____ 2. _____ 3. _____

4. _____ 5. _____ 6. _____

7. _____ 8. _____ 9. _____

Write a definition for one of the words.

_____

_____

I'm   brother   didn't   balloon   woke

second   first   birthday   can't   sister

Notes for teachers

Target: To put words into alphabetical order using the 3rd or 4th letters

Read the instructions with the pupils and ensure they understand them. Revise work on alphabetical order from the previous worksheet. Before pupils begin the task remind them that the word October starts with a capital letter as it is the name of a month. When tackling the definitions of the words it's a good idea to ask pupils to work in pairs, telling each other what they think each word means. Only after doing this should they try to write their own simple definitions.

Name: _____ **Date:** _____

Some words start with a prefix.
Read each of the words below.

most   ready   so

ways   together   one

though   mighty

Now put the prefix **al** at the beginning of each of them.

--------------------   --------------------   --------------------   --------------------

--------------------   --------------------   --------------------   --------------------

Read the new words you have made.
Write a sentence using one of your new words.

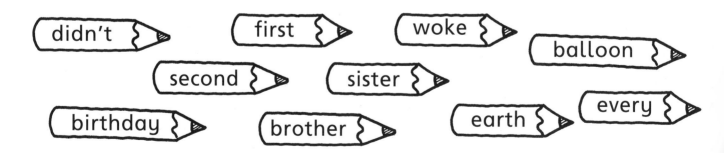

didn't   first   woke   balloon

second   sister

birthday   brother   earth   every

Notes for teachers

Target: To use the prefix **al**

Read the instructions with the pupils and ensure they understand what they are being asked to do. Help the children read the words. It is important that they form the letters **a** and **l** correctly when writing out the new words. When they have read the words encourage the pupils to put them into spoken sentences, then to choose one of these sentences to write down correctly.

Match each word from the cake with the correct clue.
The first one has been done for you.

___also___	as well
_____	nearly
_____	before the expected time
_____	with no one else
_____	at the same time

Write a sentence using one of the **al** words.

_____

_____

Notes for teachers

Target: To use the prefix **al**

Read the instructions with the pupils and ensure they understand what they have to do. Give pupils appropriate help with the task - this might include reading both the words and the clues. Remind pupils to write their sentence with a capital letter at the start and a full stop at the end.

Name: **Date:**

Many words have the letters **ed** added to them when they are put into the past tense. Complete the table below.

Present	Past
walk	walked
laugh	
	painted
wash	
play	
	opened
scream	

Write a sentence using one of the past tense words.

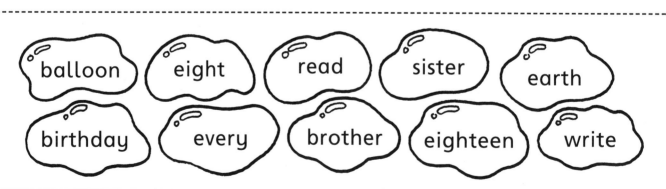

Notes for teachers

Target: To use the regular verb ending **ed**

Before starting this work revise the terms 'past tense' and 'present tense'. Read the instructions with the pupils and ensure they understand what to do. Particularly check their understanding of the word 'table' in the sense of a chart. To help children understand when to use past and present tenses ask them to create a sentence for each of the words, before and after adding the 'ed' ending – one of these sentences can then be written.

 Andrew Brodie: Supporting Literacy © A & C Black Publishers Ltd. 2006

When a word ends in **e** you need only add a **d** to put it into the past tense.

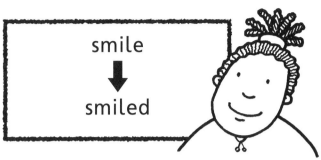

smile
↓
smiled

Put the words below into the past tense.
Some need **ed** added and some just need **d**.

Present	Past
love	
kick	
smile	
pick	
lick	
like	

Present	Past
tie	
nibble	
push	
cook	
work	
save	

brother   sister   earth   every   eight

eighteen   read   write   whole   half

Notes for teachers
Target: To use the regular verb ending **ed**
Pupils should understand that verbs are doing or action words and that it is verbs that change the tense of a sentence.
There is at least one verb in any sentence. Read the instructions with the pupils and ensure they understand what they
have to do. Read each of the words. Check that the children understand that words ending in **e** will not need another **e**
whilst the words ending with a consonant will need **ed**. Use the terms 'present tense' and 'past tense' whenever possible
and appropriate during the lesson.

Name: _____   **Date:** _____

Not all words end in **ed** for the past tense.
Choose the correct 'past tense'
word to go with each of the
'present tense' words.

ran got left
wrote gave
kept ate drew
caught met

Present	Past
get	
write	
leave	
meet	
run	
keep	
give	
catch	
eat	
draw	

earth   every   eighteen   eight   read
write   thought   whole   half   through

Notes for teachers
Target: To use/spell irregular tense changes
Before starting the task revise the work on the word ending **ed** and ask pupils if they think this will work for all verbs.
You may like to use go (went) and think (thought) as examples. Read the instructions with the pupils and ensure they
understand what they have to do. The children will find it helpful to create a sentence for each of the verbs in both the
present tense and past tense. It is important to check that pupils spell each of the past tenses correctly as they complete
the task.

Name: _____   **Date:** _____

Put the words into their correct pairs.

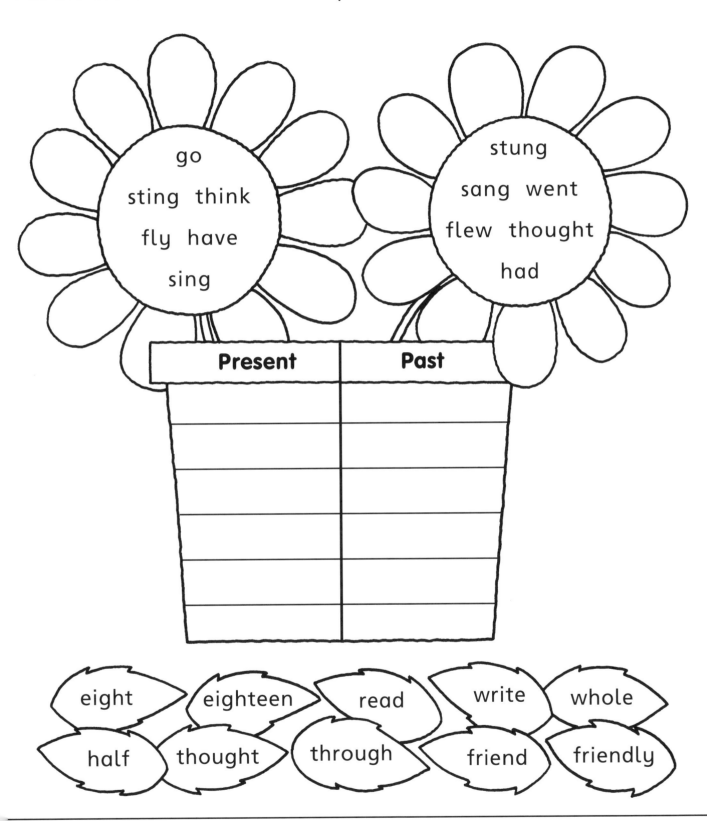

go
sting think
fly have
sing

stung
sang went
flew thought
had

Present	Past

eight   eighteen   read   write   whole

half   thought   through   friend   friendly

Notes for teachers

Target: To use/spell irregular tense changes

Revise the previous worksheet on irregular tense change. Remind pupils that it is verbs that change tense. Read the instructions with the pupils and ensure they understand what they need to do. Help the children to create a spoken sentence for each of the words. As an extension, pupils could make a bank of verbs in their present and past forms. This bank could be displayed and used as an aid to writing.

Andrew Brodie: Supporting Literacy © A & C Black Publishers Ltd. 2006   13

Name: **Date:**

All the words below end in **ight**.
Read and copy each word.

bright	flight	might	sight
---------------------	---------------------	---------------------	---------------------
night	light	tight	right
---------------------	---------------------	---------------------	---------------------

Read this sentence:

I saw a bright light
in the dark night.

Now write a sentence of your own, using as many **ight** words
as you can.

----

through   read   write   whole   friendly   white   half   friend   while   thought

Notes for teachers
Target: To spell words ending **ight**
Read the instructions with the pupils and ensure they understand them. Let the children write the letter cluster **ight** and
check that they are forming their letters correctly. Ensure that the sentence they write starts with a capital letter and ends
with a full stop.

Write the correct **ight** word by each clue.

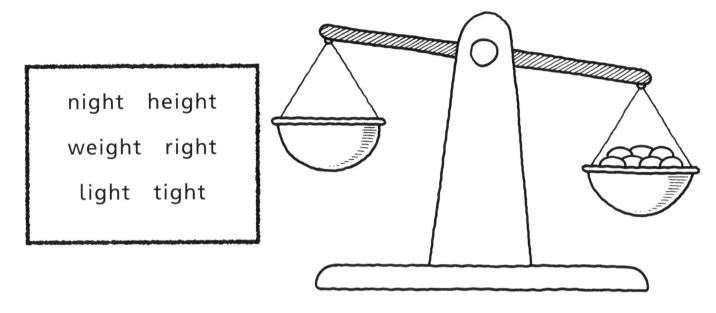

| night height |
| weight right |
| light tight |

1. Not loose: _____

2. After day: _____

3. How tall you are: _____

4. How heavy you are: _____

5. Opposite to left: _____

6. Not dark or heavy: _____

Now make up your own clue for the word bright.

_____

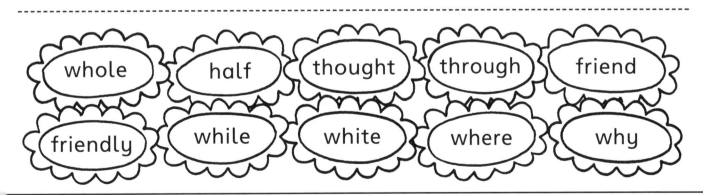

whole   half   thought   through   friend

friendly   while   white   where   why

Notes for teachers

Target: To spell words ending in **ight**

Read the instructions with the pupils and ensure they understand them. Encourage pupils to talk about possible clues for the word bright. They should make up clues that are fairly short and reflect a clear understanding of the word. This of course could be bright meaning shiny or bright meaning intelligent. If time allows let pupils investigate finding other words containing the **ight** cluster – this may be at the end of the word or in the middle.

All the words below end in **tion**.
Read and copy each word.

ration   fraction   action   auction

--------------------   --------------------   --------------------   --------------------

station   nation   attraction   decoration

--------------------   --------------------   --------------------   --------------------

Choose the correct word for each picture.

Notes for teachers

Target: To read and spell words ending in **tion**

Read the instructions with the pupils and ensure they understand what they have to do. Allow children to practise writing the letter cluster **tion** and check that they are forming the letters correctly. Talk to the pupils about what each picture represents. If there is enough time, the children could write a sentence using one of the **tion** words.

Name: **Date:**

Choose the correct word to go with each clue.

correction   creation   station

examination   fraction   decoration

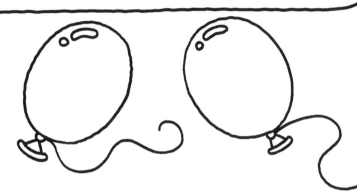

1. Something that has been put right is a: ----------------------------

2. The beginning of the world: ----------------------------

3. Part of something (perhaps half!): ----------------------------

4. A type of test: ----------------------------

5. Catch a train here: ----------------------------

Make up your own clue for the word decoration.

----

friend   while   why   white   where

friendly   heard   head   important   unimportant

Notes for teachers

Target: To read and spell words ending in **tion**

Read the instructions with the pupils and ensure they understand them. Talk to pupils about the **tion** work they did in Worksheet 11. Remind them of the importance of correct letter formation. Encourage children to talk about good clues for the word 'decoration'.

Name: **Date:**

All the words below end in **sion**.

Copy the words and then draw a picture to go with each one.

mansion

explosion

----

collision

percussion

----

while   white   unimportant   why   head

heard   important   where   know   knew

Notes for teachers

Target: To read and spell words ending in **sion**

It is important to let pupils practise writing the letters **sion**, forming each letter correctly. Read the words below the boxes with the pupils and ask them what they think each one means and what sort of picture they might wish to draw to illustrate the word. For 'percussion' it would be easy to illustrate by drawing percussion instruments (e.g. instruments that you have to shake, bang or rattle!).

Choose the correct word to go with each clue.

> collision   discussion   percussion
>
> extension   confusion   mansion

1. When things collide:

   (or bump into one another)

   ----

2. An extra piece built onto a house:

   ----

3. Drums and triangles are

   this type of instrument:

   ----

4. A muddle: ----------------------------

5. A very large house: ----------------------------

6. People talking to one another: ----------------------------

Now write your own clue for the word television.

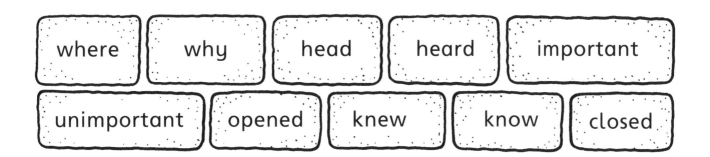

where   why   head   heard   important

unimportant   opened   knew   know   closed

Notes for teachers

Target: To read and spell words ending in **sion**

Read the clues through with the pupils and discuss the correct answers before attempting the written task. The reading practice and the understanding of the clues is as important as beginning to learn the spelling pattern.

Andrew Brodie: Supporting Literacy © A & C Black Publishers Ltd. 2006

Name: **Date:**

All the words below end in **ful**.
Read and copy each word.

beautiful   hopeful   careful

-----------------------   -----------------------   -----------------------

painful   plentiful   wonderful

-----------------------   -----------------------   -----------------------

Now draw a picture to go with the sentence below.

My sore knee is very painful.

important   head   heard   know   walk

knew   opened   walked   unimportant   closed

Notes for teachers

Target: To use and spell the word ending **ful**

Encourage children to think of as many words as they can ending in **ful**. You may like to explain that **ful** is called a suffix; it is a shortened form of the word full, added to the end of another word to create a new meaning. For example, 'careful' means full of care – the word full has been added to the end of the word care and loses a letter 'l' in the process. Remind pupils that when words end with a consonant followed by y, then 'y' is changed when an ending is added, e.g. plenty changes to 'plenti' when 'ful' is added. Ask pupils to practise writing **ful** in order to ensure they are forming the letters correctly. An additional activity could be to ask pupils to put some of the given words into sentences.

Choose the correct word to go with each clue.

WORD BOX

careful

beautiful

cheerful

hopeful

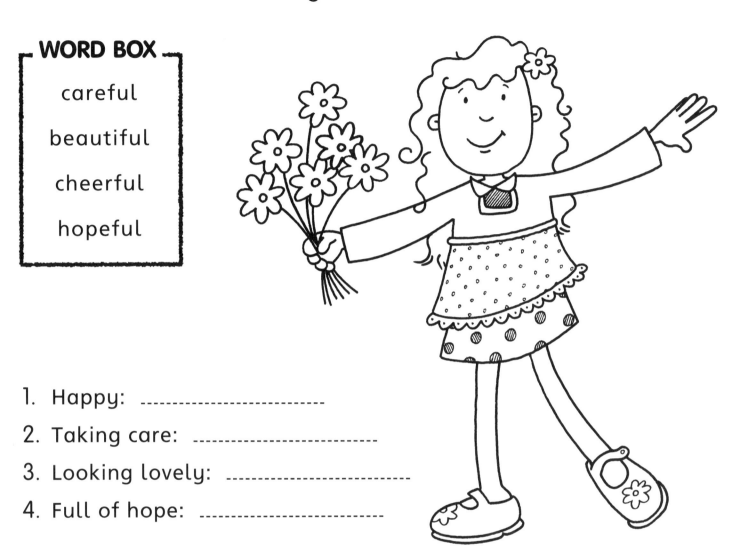

1. Happy: ....

2. Taking care: ....

3. Looking lovely: ....

4. Full of hope: ....

Write your own clue for the word painful.

....

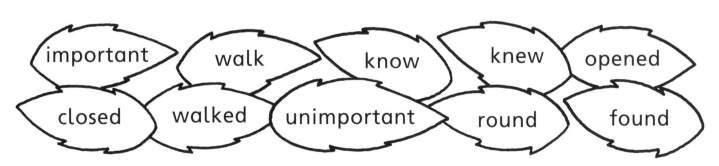

important   walk   know   knew   opened

closed   walked   unimportant   round   found

Notes for teachers

Target: To use and spell the word ending **ful**

You could again take the opportunity to remind pupils that a word ending with a consonant then 'y' is changed when an ending is added, for example 'beauty' changes to 'beauti' when 'ful' is added. An extra activity would be for pupils to think of more **ful** words and make up clues for them.

Name: _____ **Date:** _____

Many words end in **ious**. They can be tricky words to spell.
Read each of the words below.
Write each one twice.

mysterious

----

curious   previous

-----------------------------   -----------------------------

-----------------------------   -----------------------------

obvious   anxious   hilarious

-------------   -------------   -------------

-------------   -------------   -------------

Write a sentence using one of the **ious** words.

----

something   knew   opened   closed   know

walked   round   sometimes   found   walk

Notes for teachers
Target: To read and spell the word ending **ious**
Read the instructions with the pupils and ensure they understand them. Help the children read the words before asking them to complete the activity. Give children the opportunity to practise writing the letter cluster **ious**, ensuring of course that the letters are correctly formed.

    Andrew Brodie: Supporting Literacy © A & C Black Publishers Ltd. 2006

Write the correct word by each clue.

WORD BANK

anxious   precious   mysterious

hilarious   fractious   tedious

1. Fearful or worried: _____

2. Boring: _____

3. Extremely funny: _____

4. Full of mystery: _____

5. Bad tempered or irritable: _____

6. Very valuable: _____

Write a clue of your own for the word 'previous'.

_____

opened 😊   closed 😊   something 😊   walked 😊   round 😊

😊 found   😊 walk   😊 sometimes   😊 stopped   😊 started

Notes for teachers
Target: To read and spell the word ending **ious**
The children will need plenty of support in reading these difficult words and in reading the clues that go with them but this activity provides an excellent opportunity for practice. Encourage the pupils to talk about what sort of clue they might make up for the word 'previous'. Note that they do not need to write the clue as a sentence.

All the words below end in **ive**.

Copy the words and then draw a picture to go with each one.

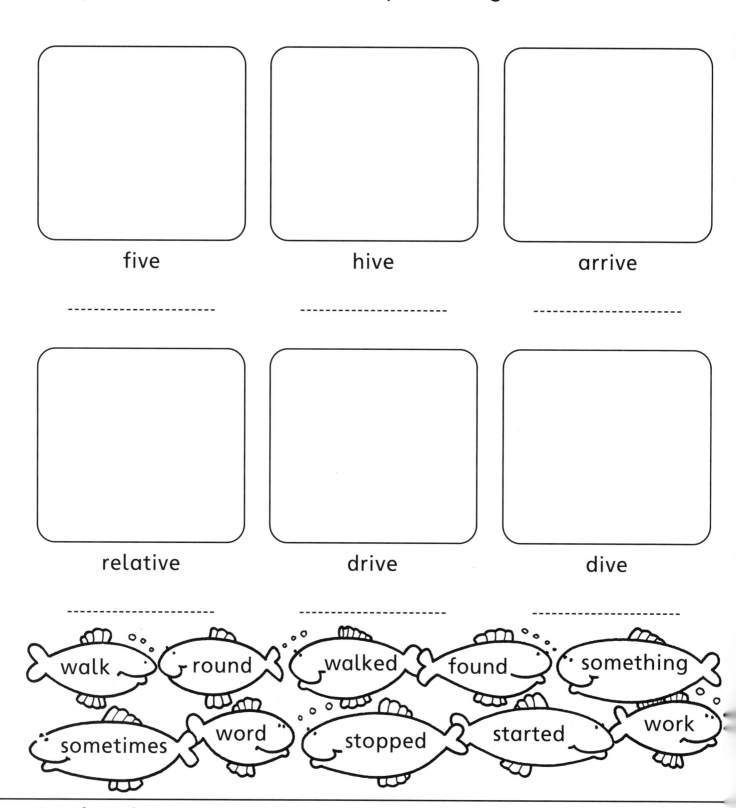

five

hive

arrive

- -

- -

- -

relative

drive

dive

- -

- -

- -

walk   round   walked   found   something

sometimes   word   stopped   started   work

Notes for teachers

Target: To read and spell words ending in **ive**

Read the instructions with the pupils and ensure they understand them. Ask pupils to practise writing the letters 'ive' to check that they are forming their letters correctly. As an extension activity you could ask the children to make up a sentence to go with one of the words.

Andrew Brodie: Supporting Literacy © A & C Black Publishers Ltd. 2006

Name: _____ **Date:** _____

Write the correct **ive** word beside each clue.

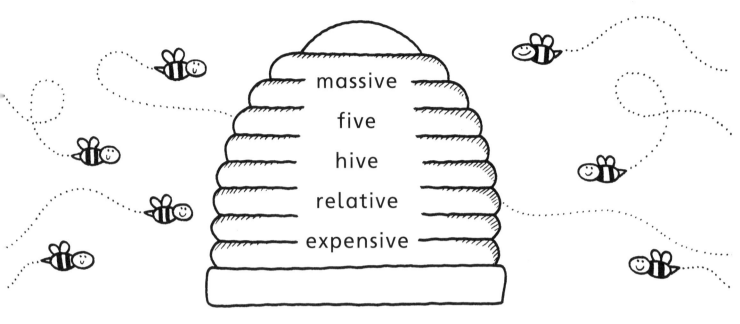

massive

five

hive

relative

expensive

1. Huge: _____

2. Costing a lot of money: _____

3. One more than four: _____

4. Find bees here: _____

5. A member of the family: _____

Now write your own clue for the word 'alive'.

_____

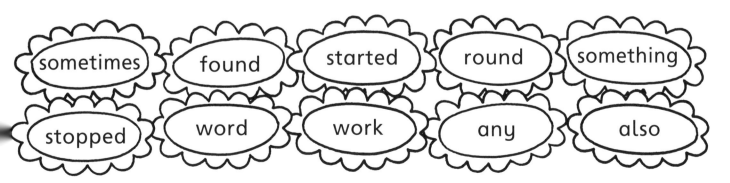

sometimes   found   started   round   something

stopped   word   work   any   also

Notes for teachers

Target: to read and spell words ending in **ive**

Read the instructions with the pupils and ensure they understand them. Let pupils discuss possible clues for the word 'alive' before attempting to fill in their clue on the worksheet. Note that they do not need to write the clue as a sentence.

Andrew Brodie: Supporting Literacy © A & C Black Publishers Ltd. 2006   25

Name: **Date:**

All the words below end in **ough**.
Read and copy each word.

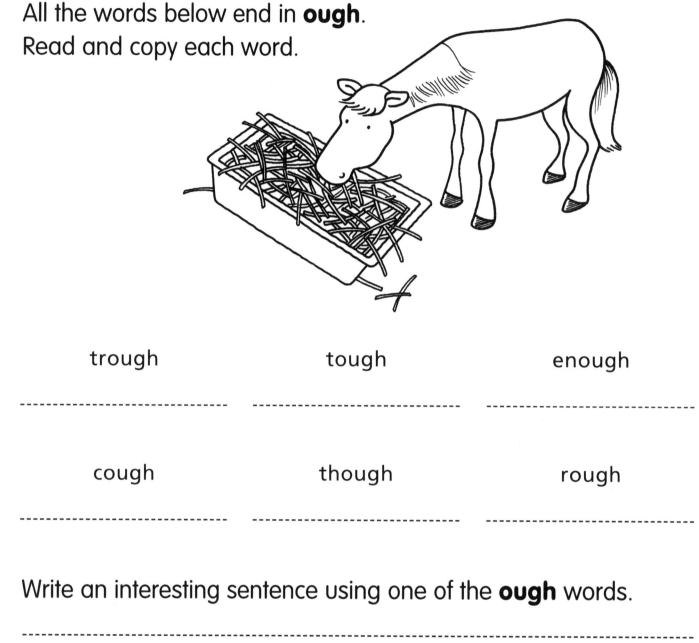

trough   tough   enough

----------------------------   ----------------------------   ----------------------------

cough   though   rough

----------------------------   ----------------------------   ----------------------------

Write an interesting sentence using one of the **ough** words.

Notes for teachers
Target: To read and spell words ending in **ough**
Encourage pupils to practise writing the letters 'ough' to check they are forming their letters correctly. Read the words through carefully with the pupils and discuss the fact that **ough** can sound different in different words, e.g. cough and plough.

Read the **ough** words carefully.

Choose the correct word to go with each of the pictures.

------------------------   ------------------------

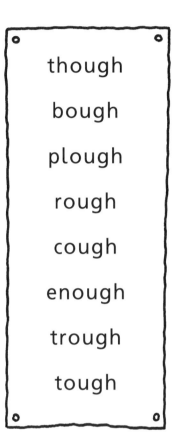

though

bough

plough

rough

cough

enough

trough

tough

----------------------------   ----------------------------

Now put the words from the box into alphabetical order.

---------------------   ---------------------   ---------------------   ---------------------

---------------------   ---------------------   ---------------------   ---------------------

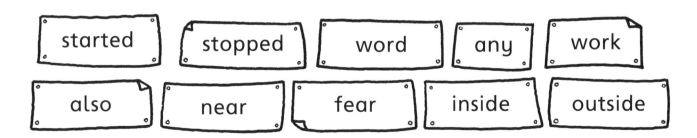

started   stopped   word   any   work

also   near   fear   inside   outside

Notes for teachers

Target: To read and spell words ending in **ough**

It is important to read each of the eight given words and discuss their meaning. Remind pupils of the importance of copying the words correctly when they sort them into alphabetical order.

Name: **Date:**

Some words are made from two or more shorter words.
These are called compound words.
The words at the top can be put with the words in the boxes to make new compound words.

house   goose   out   board   black

straw   fly   smith   cake   mail

green ------------------

green ------------------

cup ------------------

cup ------------------

------------------ berry

------------------ berry

------------------ berry

black ------------------

black ------------------

black ------------------

word   work   any   also   near

fear   inside   outside   used   useful

Notes for teachers
Target: To recognise compound words and to use them as an aid to spelling
Talk to pupils about using their knowledge of shorter words to help them to spell the longer compound words. Creating a spoken sentence for each word provides excellent practice of speaking and listening as well as preparing the pupils for writing a clear, well-constructed sentence.

Andrew Brodie: Supporting Literacy © A & C Black Publishers Ltd. 2006

Compound words are made from two or more shorter words.
Use the words at the top to make new words in the boxes
underneath.

meal   bin   child   pan   hand   some

man   parent   cart   brake   stand   some

grand --------------------

grand --------------------

grand --------------------

hand --------------------

-------------------- bag

hand --------------------

dust --------------------

dust --------------------

dust --------------------

dust --------------------

whole --------------------

whole --------------------

any

outside

also

used

near

useful

fear

own

inside

owner

Notes for teachers
Target: to recognise compound words and to use them as an aid to spelling
Note the word 'some' is in the word box twice for 'handsome' and 'wholesome'. An extra activity would be to make a
bank of compound words. This could be arranged in alphabetical order and displayed on the wall as a writing aid.

Name:

Date:

An **adverb** is a word which describes a verb.

Many **adverbs** end in **ly**.

Write a short sentence for each adverb.

The first one has been done for you.

Quickly: ......*The dog ran quickly down the road.*....................

Happily: ....

Loudly: ....

Wearily: ....

Accidentally: ....

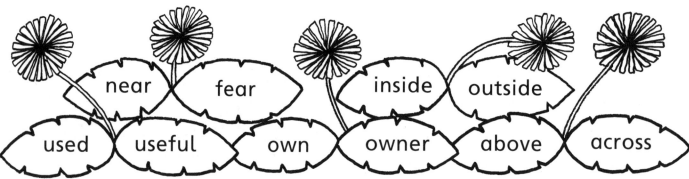

near   fear   inside   outside

used   useful   own   owner   above   across

Notes for teachers

Target: to understand the term 'adverb'

Before tackling the task, ensure the children understand what a verb is. Read the instructions through carefully with the pupils ensuring that they have a clear understanding of what an adverb is. Use the terms 'verb' and 'adverb' frequently throughout this task. Pupils should do this work orally before writing anything on their worksheet. The sentences must start with capital letters and end with full stops.

    Andrew Brodie: Supporting Literacy © A & C Black Publishers Ltd. 2006

Name: _____   **Date:** _____

Choose the adverb from the list that best describes each verb.
The first one has been done for you. Use each adverb only once.

1. He ran ....<u>quickly</u>..........

2. They whispered ....

3. She laughed ....

4. The lamp glowed ....

5. Mum frowned ....

6. He crept ....

7. They worked ....

~~quickly~~

carefully

brightly

happily

crossly

quietly

slowly

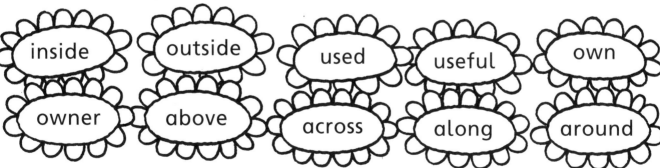

inside   outside   used   useful   own

owner   above   across   along   around

Notes for teachers
Target: To understand the term 'adverb'
Read the instructions with the pupils and ensure they understand them. Before writing in the answers check the pupils'
understanding of the terms 'verb' and 'adverb'. You could ask pupils to underline each of the verbs given in the seven
sentences. As an extension activity the children could make up their own sentences using one or more of the words.

Name: **Date:**

An **adjective** is a word used to describe something.
Choose the best adjective from the list to describe each item
below. You can use each adjective only once.
The first one has been done for you.

lion .... *fierce* ....

tree ....

fire ....

light ....

dinner ....

test ....

kangaroo ....

leaf ....

clown ....

sofa ....

green

~~fierce~~

comfortable

funny

tasty

difficult

bright

bouncy

hot

tall

across   useful   own   owner   above

used   along   around   ask   answer

Notes for teachers
Target: To understand the term 'adjective'
Read the instructions with the pupils and ensure they understand them. You may ask pupils to give you examples of
adjectives – perhaps adjectives to describe their hair or a feature of the classroom. Use the term 'adjective' frequently
during this work. As an extension activity the children could make up their own sentences using one or more of the words.

Read the sentences carefully. Look for the **adjective**, or **adjectives**, in each sentence. Underline each adjective in red.

1. My little kitten has soft fur.

2. I read an interesting book.

3. The colourful flag waved in the wind.

4. She put small logs on the blazing fire.

5. I ate a juicy orange and a crunchy apple.

6. I enjoyed a good chat with my best friend.

Now find all the **nouns** and underline them in green.

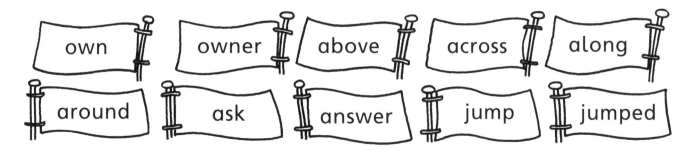

| own | owner | above | across | along |
| around | ask | answer | jump | jumped |

Notes for teachers
Target: To understand the term 'adjective'
Read the instructions with the pupils and ensure they understand what they have to do. Revise the work done on adjectives on Worksheet 27. Pupils should underline carefully, using a ruler, to produce a straight line for each adjective. Before tackling the final part of the task, talk with pupils about what a noun is.

Name: _____   Date: _____

Nouns often have an **s** added to show there is more than one.
Add an **s** to change each of these words from **singular** to **plural**.

house __   garden __   hand __

cup __   bird __   stick __

table __   bell __   book __

Read the plural words you have made.
Use one of the plural words in an interesting or funny sentence.

above   across   ask   along   around

answer   jump   jumped   sudden   suddenly

Notes for teachers
Target: To use the terms 'singular' and 'plural'; to begin to investigate how spellings may change when a noun becomes a plural.
Read the instructions with the pupils and ensure they understand what to do. It is important to revise the meaning of the word 'noun'. Make sure that pupils have an understanding of the words 'singular' and 'plural'.

For some words you need to add more than
s to make them plural.
Choose the plural word from the box that
goes with each of the singular words given.

geese   pennies   puppies   potatoes   knives

flies   leaves   tomatoes   brushes   sheep

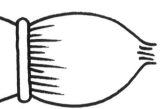

Singular	Plural
leaf	
knife	
puppy	
brush	
tomato	

Singular	Plural
goose	
fly	
sheep	
potato	
penny	

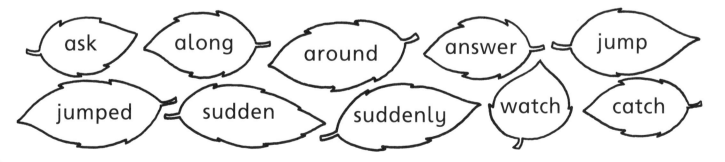

ask   along   around   answer   jump

jumped   sudden   suddenly   watch   catch

Notes for teachers
Target: To use the terms 'singular' and 'plural'; to begin to investigate how spellings may change when a noun becomes
a plural.
Read the instructions with the pupils and ensure they understand them. Ask pupils to think of other nouns that do not just
have a letter 's' to make them plural. Encourage children to look for patterns in plurals, eg a final **f** becoming **ves**, or
removing the **y** and adding **ies**.

Notes for teachers

The next four worksheets are to be used for pupils to write sentences unaided. They can make use of the dictionary card on pages 57 to 60 of this book. You may also like to have some specific word lists available to which the pupils can refer, e.g. the months of the year.

Each worksheet will feature a dictation exercise that an adult reads out loud. The adult may need to allow time for the pupils to make use of their dictionary card.

The first exercise consists of short sentences containing several words from the NLS medium frequency word list recommended for Years 4 and 5. In the second exercise the sentences include the need to write capital letters for the months of the year; this work also features a short list separated by a comma and the word 'and'. The third and fourth exercises include speech marks, question marks and exclamation marks.

Exercise 1

I do lots of things at the weekend. Sometimes I play outside in the garden. Sometimes I go swimming. Sometimes I stay inside and just look out of the window.

Exercise 2

Most people go on holiday in the summer. They usually go in July or August when schools are closed. Not many people go on holiday in the autumn because it gets cold in September, October and November.

Exercise 3

"Where is the baby?" asked Mum.

"He has gone outside," I replied.

"He shouldn't go outside on his own," said Mum. She ran outside to find him.

Exercise 4

"Have you got any homework?" asked Dad.

"Not much," said Tom. "I have got to write a story about a lady who can fly."

"Do you know any ladies who can fly?" asked Dad.

"Only Mum," replied Tom.

Andrew Brodie: Supporting Literacy © A & C Black Publishers Ltd. 2006

Notes for teachers

Target: To write sentences using capital letters and full stops appropriately; to make use of a dictionary card to assist with spelling.

This is dictation Exercise 1 (see page 36). The exercise consists of four simple sentences containing mainly words from the NLS list of medium frequency words for Years 4 and 5. You will need to read each sentence several times, offering lots of encouragement to the pupils and allowing them time to look up spellings on the dictionary card made from pages 00 to 00 of this book. Remind pupils that each sentence starts with a capital letter and ends with a full stop.

Andrew Brodie: Supporting Literacy © A & C Black Publishers Ltd. 2006

jump jumped much such with without

catch sudden suddenly watch

Notes for teachers

Target: To write sentences using capital letters and full stops appropriately; to use capital letters for the initial letters of the months of the year; to make use of a dictionary card to assist with spelling; to use commas in a list.

This is dictation Exercise 2 (see page 36) which contains three sentences that include the names of five months of the year. The third sentence includes three months in a list. You will need to introduce this by showing written examples of words in a list, e.g. Yesterday I bought apples, oranges, and bananas. Point out that there are three items in the list but only one comma – with lists we write commas after each item except the last two where we use the word 'and'. You will need to read each sentence several times, offering lots of encouragement and allowing pupils plenty of time to look up spellings on the dictionary card (pages 00 to 00). Remind them that each sentence starts with a capital letter and ends with a full stop and that the months of the year need initial capitals.

Andrew Brodie: Supporting Literacy © A & C Black Publishers Ltd. 2006

- -

- -

- -

- -

- -

- -

Notes for teachers

Target: To write sentences using capital letters and full stops appropriately; to add question marks or exclamation marks to sentences; to begin to use speech marks; to make use of a dictionary card to assist with spelling.

This is dictation Exercise 3 (see page 36). The exercise consists of four sentences. The punctuation of these sentences is much more complicated than the punctuation in the previous two exercises. You may like to show the pupils the written sentences before dictating them. Point out the use of speech marks; show them the question mark in the first sentence that must be placed before the closing speech marks of Mum's question; show them the comma in the second sentence that must be placed before the closing speech marks of the child's reply. Discuss the use of the apostrophe in the word 'shouldn't' in the third sentence – this apostrophe has been used to replace the letter o in the word 'not'.

----

watch   catch   much   such   with

without   try   tries   those   these

Notes for teachers

Target: To write sentences using capital letters and full stops appropriately; to add question marks and exclamation marks to sentences; to begin to use speech marks; to make use of a dictionary card to assist with spelling.

This exercise provides further practice of the use of speech marks, question marks and commas. You may like to show the pupils the written sentences before dictating them. Point out the use of speech marks; show them that for each piece of direct speech there is always another punctuation mark **before** the closing speech marks: a question mark, a comma or a full stop.

Andrew Brodie: Supporting Literacy © A & C Black Publishers Ltd. 2006

You will need some of these words in your history and geography lessons.

Victorians   Greece   cycle
Tudor   Britain   ~~globe~~   route
~~atlas~~   mountain   exploration
ancient   atlases   environment
~~coast~~   ~~river~~   water

Write the words in the correct alphabetical order on the list.
Some of the words are already in place for you.
Draw rings round the letters that don't have any words in the list.

a b c d e f g h i j k l m
n o p q r s t u v w x y z

a _____
_____ atlas _____
_____
b _____
c _____ coast _____
_____
e _____
_____
g _____ globe _____
_____
m _____
r _____ river _____
_____
t _____
v _____ Victorians _____
w _____

such   with   those   try
much   tries   without   these   right   might

Notes for teachers
Target: To read and spell words associated with history and geography topics covered in Y6
This page provides the opportunity to learn to read and spell vocabulary that will be used in history and geography lessons. It also offers useful practice of arranging words in alphabetical order. Explain to the children that 'ancient' comes before 'atlas' because 'n' comes before 't' and that 'atlas' comes before 'atlases'. You could discuss the words with the children, checking that they know what each word means. They can also find some words that go together, eg Ancient Greece; Tudor exploration; water cycle.

Name: **Date:**

You will need some of these words in your science lessons.

~~predator~~ ~~consumer~~	
producer order	
battery wire bulb	
circuit ~~batteries~~	
evaporation series	
diagram ~~switch~~	

b .... _batteries_ ....

_____

_____

c _____

.... _consumer_ ....

d _____

e _____

o _____

p .... _predator_ ....

_____

s _____

.... _switch_ ....

w _____

Write the words in the correct alphabetical order. Some of the words are already in place for you.

Draw rings round the letters that don't have any words in the list.

a b c d e f g h i j k l m n o p q r s t u v w x y z

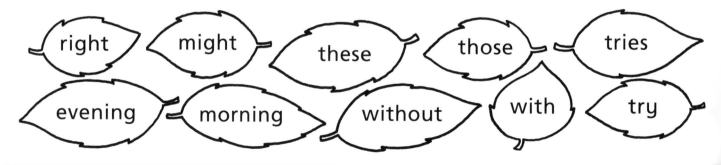

right   might   these   those   tries

evening   morning   without   with   try

Notes for teachers

Target: To read and spell words associated with science covered in Y6

This page provides the opportunity to learn to read and spell vocabulary that will be used in science lessons. It also offers useful practice of arranging words in alphabetical order. Discuss with the children why 'batteries' comes before 'battery'. You may need to discuss the words with the children, checking that they know what each word means.

Name: _____ **Date:** _____

a b c d e f g h i j k l m n o p q r s t u v w x y z

You need to be able to spell these words.

a .... _above_ ....

....

....

.... _along_ ....

....

....

.... _animals_ ....

....

....

....

b ....

.... _balloon_ ....

....

.... _being_ ....

....

.... _between_ ....

began	across	brought	also
~~above~~	can't	~~animals~~	birthday
around	asked	~~balloon~~	before
almost	both	better	~~along~~
~~being~~	below	always	~~between~~
~~brother~~	baby	change	any

Write the words in the correct alphabetical order on the list. Some of the words are already in place for you.

....

....

.... _brother_ ....

....

c ....

....

Notes for teachers
Target: To read and spell words from the NLS medium frequency list; to arrange words in alphabetical order.
This page provides the opportunity to learn to read and spell twenty-four of the NLS medium frequency words. It also offers useful practice in arranging words in alphabetical order. Because many of the words begin with the same letter the children will need to look at second, third or fourth letters. You may need to discuss the words with the children, checking that they know what each word means.

Name: _____

Date: _____

a b c d e f g h i j k l m n o p q r s t u v w x y z

You need to be able to spell these words.

c ....

....

....

d ....

....

........_does_........

....

....

e ....

....

....

f ...._father_........

....

....

........._found_........

....

g ....

........._goes_........

happy	clothes	first	didn't
don't	half	during	earth
~~goes~~	every	~~father~~	friends
coming	garden	different	great
children	~~found~~	~~does~~	~~gone~~
~~head~~	follow	eyes	heard

Write the words in the correct alphabetical order. Some of the words are already in place for you.

........._gone_........

....

h ....

....

........._head_........

....

Notes for teachers

Target: To read and spell words from the NLS medium frequency list; to arrange words in alphabetical order.

This page provides the opportunity to learn to read and spell twenty-four of the NLS medium frequency words. It also offers useful practice of arranging words in alphabetical order. Because many of the words begin with the same letter the children will need to look at second, third or fourth letters. You may need to discuss the words with the children, checking that they know what each word means.

Andrew Brodie: Supporting Literacy © A & C Black Publishers Ltd. 2006

Name: _____   **Date:** _____

a b c d e f g h i j k l m n o p q r s t u v w x y z

You need to be able to spell these words.

h _____

i _____ I'm _____

_____

_____

j _____

k _____ Knew _____

l _____

_____

_____

m _____

_____ money _____

_____

_____

_____ much _____

n _____

_____

_____ number _____

I'm   money   inside   knew

much   leave   number   often

might   know   mother   never

only   other   light   important

outside   near   morning   own

lady   high   jumped   opened

Write the words in the correct alphabetical order. Some of the words are already in place for you.

o _____

_____

_____ opened _____

_____

_____

_____

Notes for teachers

Target: To read and spell words from the NLS medium frequency list; to arrange words in alphabetical order.

This page provides the opportunity to learn to read and spell twenty-four of the NLS medium frequency words. It also offers useful practice of arranging words in alphabetical order. Because some of the words begin with the same letter the children will need to look at second, third or fourth letters. You may need to discuss the words with the children, checking that they know what each word means.

Name: **Date:**

a b c d e f g h i j k l m n o p q r s t u v w x y z

You need to be able to spell these words.

p _____

_____

r _____

_____

s _____

_____ show _____

_____

_____ small _____

_____

_____ something _____

_____

_____ started _____

_____

_____ such _____

_____

_____ swimming _____

---

sure   place   round   ~~such~~   second

those   still   ~~show~~   stopped   sister

right   ~~something~~   sometimes

~~started~~   ~~small~~   together   paper

~~through~~   thought   ~~swimming~~

suddenly   ~~think~~   sound   today

Write the words in the correct alphabetical order. Some of the words are already in place for you.

t _____ think _____

_____

_____

_____ through _____

_____

_____

Notes for teachers

Target: To read and spell words from the NLS medium frequency list; to arrange words in alphabetical order.
This page provides the opportunity to learn to read and spell twenty-four of the NLS medium frequency words. It also offers useful practice of arranging words in alphabetical order. Because some of the words begin with the same letter the children will need to look at second, third or fourth letters. You may need to discuss the words with the children, checking that they know what each word means.

a b c d e f g h i j k l m n o p q r s t u v w x y z

You need to be able to spell these words.

| t _____ |
| _____ |
| _____ |
| u _____ |
| _____ |
| _____ upon _____ |
| _____ |
| w _____ |
| _____ walked _____ |
| _____ |
| _____ |
| _____ while _____ |
| _____ |
| _____ why _____ |
| _____ |
| _____ woke _____ |

| window   write   tries   word |
| turn   under   ~~walked~~   watch |
| year   where   told   without |
| used   young   ~~woke~~   ~~upon~~ |
| ~~white~~   white   ~~work~~   whole |
| world   walk   ~~why~~   until |

Write the words in the correct alphabetical order. Some of the words are already in place for you.

| _____ work _____ |
| _____ |
| y _____ |
| _____ |

Dictionary

Notes for teachers

Target: To read and spell words from the NLS medium frequency list; to arrange words in alphabetical order.

This page provides the opportunity to learn to read and spell twenty-four of the NLS medium frequency words. It also offers useful practice of arranging words in alphabetical order. Because some of the words begin with the same letter the children will need to look at second, third or fourth letters. You may need to discuss the words with the children, checking that they know what each word means.

Brodie's Second Reading Test for Medium Frequency Words

The NLS recommends that children learn specified lists of high frequency words during KS1 and a specified list of medium frequency words during Years 4 and 5. Please note that, for some reason, the Literacy Strategy includes some words on both lists.

Some of the pupils who are receiving extra support in Year 6 will still be in the process of learning the words from the KS1 lists and with these pupils you may wish to use the recognition tests for high frequency words that are included in *Supporting Literacy for ages 7-8 and 8-9*.

In this book we incorporate a word recognition test especially for the medium frequency words recommended for Years 4 and 5. The reading test takes the form of a story of appropriate interest level entitled 'Sailing Away to Sea'. The story includes every word from the list of medium frequency words for Years 4 and 5, many with repeats, plus most of the words from the list for Reception and most of the words from the high frequency list for Years 1 and 2 (apart from some of the days of the week, months of the year, numbers to twenty, colours and addresses). Obviously we have had to include some words that are not in the high frequency or medium frequency word lists but many of which are closely related to the words in the lists.

The story is printed once for the child to read, and once with a hundred of the Year 4 and 5 target words in bold type with a box next to them. This is for you to use as an assessment sheet to record the sight recognition of these medium frequency words. Simply tick the box for each word that is read correctly. Find the total number of correct words and this will provide you with a percentage score for the test. You could carry out this assessment twice during the school year, thus enabling you to make a judgement of each individual pupil's progress.

We suggest that you read the whole story to the pupil before asking him or her to attempt it. If you find that the pupil needs prompting on more than two or three words per sentence you may decide that the test is too demanding in which case you could try the test in *Supporting Literacy for ages 8-9*.

You may decide to assess the pupil on just one page of the story – each page includes twenty-five of the target words so that you can gain a percentage score by multiplying the number of correct target words that the pupil reads by four. You could spread the assessment over two or four sessions. On each occasion, remind the pupil of the story encouraging him or her to practise reading it. Although it is designed as an assessment, the story can be used as an effective tool in learning the target words. You may also like to make use of the 'flashcards' that can be made from pages 61 to 64 of this book.

After a pupil has completed the reading test he/she could answer questions about the story. For example:

How old was Kate when the family first set sail?

For how long did the family stay in New Zealand?

What did they live in when they were in New Zealand?

What present did Kate have for her birthday?

Why do you think that she was so pleased with this present?

What do you think had made the bubbles that Kate saw?

Andrew Brodie: Supporting Literacy © A & C Black Publishers Ltd. 2006

Associated words (not included in the NLS lists)

adventure	country	joking	quick	sleep
afternoon	cross	Kate	read	splash
against	crossly	land	really	stars
ago	dangerous	lapping	reply	stay
Australia	dark	living	route	stayed
beach	decided	lots	running	swam
beautiful	deck	lovely	sail	telling
behind	describe	making	sailed	things
birds	each	map	sailing	though
boat	even	moving	screamed	tip
bob	excitement	nearly	screams	Tom
books	fill	New Zealand	seas	top
bought	fish	nice	set	truth
bright	globe	packed	shape	types
brightly	halfway	pencils	sharks	waves
bubbles	huge	planet	shining	wetsuit
cloud	hurt	playing	shouted	which
coast	into	pounds	side	wrong
countries	islands	present	sky	younger

Words from the Reception list included in the story

a	for	it	on	this
all	get	like	play	to
and	go	look	said	up
at	he	me	see	was
big	I	mum	she	we
dad	in	my	the	went
day	is	of	they	you

Words for Y1 and Y2 included in the story

about	can't	him	out	very
after	could	his	saw	way
again	do	house	school	were
an	don't	if	sister	what
another	down	jump	so	when
as	first	just	some	where
back	from	much	that	who
be	good	must	their	will
because	got	night	them	with
bed	had	not	then	would
been	half	now	there	your
brother	has	old	time	
but	have	one	too	
came	her	or	two	

Brodie's Second Reading Test for Medium Frequency Words

Teacher's record sheet

Name of pupil: _____   Date of test: _____

Date of birth: _____   Year group: _____   Percentage score: ____

Sailing Away to Sea

When Kate was very **young** ☐ and her **brother** ☐ Tom was just a baby, their **mother** ☐ and father **started** ☐ a great adventure. They bought a big boat and set off to sail **around** ☐ the **whole** ☐ world. That was **almost** ☐ nine years ago so Kate is now eleven years old and Tom is nine.

When they **first** ☐ set out they sailed **across** ☐ to France. Mum and Dad didn't **know** ☐ so much about sailing in **those** ☐ days so they stayed **near** ☐ the coast. After a while they **began** ☐ to get **much** ☐ better. They sailed across many seas to a huge **number** ☐ of countries. They had to **change** ☐ their pounds for different types of **money** ☐ in nearly every country.

The **earth** ☐ is a very big planet and when they got about halfway **round** ☐ they **stopped** ☐ at New Zealand. They thought it was **such** ☐ a nice **place** ☐ they stayed there for two years.

While they were in New Zealand Kate went to school and made some good **friends** ☐. Tom was younger than his sister so he stayed at home. They lived in a small house but they had a **garden** ☐ so they could play **outside** ☐.

Kate and Tom were **happy** ☐ there but, after a **while** ☐, Mum and Dad decided that they wanted a change. They **asked** ☐ the children if they would like to set sail again.

"I like **being** ☐ here so half of me wants to stay here," said Kate, "and **half** ☐ of me wants to go! **I'm** ☐ not **sure** ☐ what I want."

Tom was **still** ☐ small but he **jumped** ☐ up and down with excitement. "I like the land but it's much **better** ☐ at sea," he said.

So the family packed their **clothes** ☐ into their boat and set sail again. First they decided to **head** ☐ for Australia but then they **turned** ☐ to **follow** ☐ a different route. Every day Mum would **show** ☐ Kate where they were on a map.

One day it was Kate's **birthday** ☐. Mum and Dad gave her a big present. When she **opened** ☐ it she **found** ☐ a big globe. "**Today** ☐ is a **great** ☐ day," said Kate, "I have got my very **own** ☐ globe."

They found some lovely islands **where** ☐ the sea was bright blue and the sun shone brightly **every** ☐ day, **without** ☐ a cloud in the sky. They stayed there for three years, living on their boat **near** ☐ a beautiful beach.

Andrew Brodie: Supporting Literacy © A & C Black Publishers Ltd. 2006

Sometimes ☐ they would sleep on deck at night with the sea **below** ☐ them and the only **light** ☐ coming from the stars shining high **above** ☐ them. Sometimes they would go to bed **inside** ☐ the boat and look out at the sea **through** ☐ the window before they went to sleep. They would be **woken** ☐ the next day by the **sound** ☐ of the waves lapping against the side of the boat.

During ☐ the **morning** ☐ the children had to do school **work** ☐. Mum and Dad had **brought** ☐ books for them to read and **also** ☐ paper and pencils. Kate would **write** ☐ about all the things that she had seen. She **used** ☐ lovely words to describe the sea and the sky and the birds and the fish.

Every afternoon the children could go **swimming** ☐. They **often** ☐ took a ball or a **balloon** ☐ to play with in the water. They would try to push the ball **right** ☐ under the water. They had lots of **tries** ☐ but the ball would **always** ☐ bob back up again. Sometimes Kate would fill the balloon with water. She would walk through the sea behind Tom so that he **didn't** ☐ see her **coming** ☐ then, suddenly, she would tip the water all over him **before** ☐ he had time to **turn** ☐ round.

The brother and sister got **along** ☐ very well **together** ☐. Sometimes, though, they would get cross with each other.

"**Don't** ☐ splash me," Tom would say. "The water **goes** ☐ in my eyes."

"I **can't** ☐ help it," Kate would reply, but she **knew** ☐ she was making Tom cross. "Anyway, even if it **does** ☐ go in your eyes it won't hurt you."

One day the children were playing in the water when Tom **told** ☐ Kate that he had seen some sharks. Kate didn't **think** ☐ that Tom was telling the truth **until** ☐ she saw lots of **white** ☐ bubbles **upon** ☐ the top of the water.

"Quick, Tom, it's **important** ☐, we must **leave** ☐ the water this **second** ☐!" shouted Kate.

"Why?" asked Tom.

"Because you saw some sharks."

"I didn't see **any** ☐ really," said Tom.

"You should **never** ☐ lie to me," said Kate crossly.

"I was **only** ☐ joking."

Kate decided to keep **watch** ☐ because she had seen the bubbles and there might be a shark or another dangerous animal. The bubbles had **gone** ☐ now but something was moving in the water. Kate **thought** ☐ of all the animals and fish that live in the sea – which one could it be?

Suddenly a dark shape swam **between** ☐ Kate and Tom. They **both** ☐ screamed. Mum and Dad **heard** ☐ the screams and came running down the beach to see what was wrong. They both laughed when a **lady** ☐ in a wetsuit came out of the water and walked up the beach!

Pupil's sheet

Sailing away to sea

When Kate was very young and her brother Tom was just a baby, their mother and father started a great adventure. They bought a big boat and set off to sail around the whole world. That was almost nine years ago so Kate is now eleven years old and Tom is nine.

When they first set out they sailed across to France. Mum and Dad didn't know so much about sailing in those days so they stayed near the coast. After a while they began to get much better. They sailed across many seas to a huge number of countries. They had to change their pounds for different types of money in nearly every country.

The earth is a very big planet and when they got about halfway round they stopped at New Zealand. They thought it was such a nice place they stayed there for two years.

While they were in New Zealand Kate went to school and made some good friends. Tom was younger than his sister so he stayed at home. They lived in a small house but they had a garden so they could play outside.

Kate and Tom were happy there but, after a while, Mum and Dad decided that they wanted a change. They asked the children if they would like to set sail again.

"I like being here so half of me wants to stay here," said Kate, "and half of me wants to go! I'm not sure what I want."

Tom was still small but he jumped up and down with excitement. "I like the land but it's much better at sea," he said.

So the family packed their clothes into their boat and set sail again. First they decided to head for Australia but then they turned to follow a different route. Every day Mum would show Kate where they were on a map.

One day it was Kate's birthday. Mum and Dad gave her a big present. When she opened it she found a big globe. "Today is a great day," said Kate, "I have got my very own globe."

They found some lovely islands where the sea was bright blue and the sun shone brightly every day, without a cloud in the sky. They stayed there for three years, living on their boat near a beautiful beach.

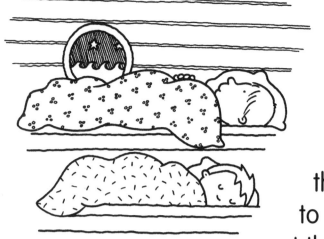

Sometimes they would sleep on deck at night with the sea below them and the only light coming from the stars shining high above them. Sometimes they would go to bed inside the boat and look out at the sea through the window before they went to sleep. They would be woken the next day by the sound of the waves lapping against the side of the boat.

During the morning the children had to do school work. Mum and Dad had brought books for them to read and also paper and pencils. Kate would write about all the things that she had seen. She used lovely words to describe the sea and the sky and the birds and the fish.

Every afternoon the children could go swimming. They often took a ball or a balloon to play with in the water. They would try to push the ball right under the water. They had lots of tries but the ball would always bob back up again. Sometimes Kate would fill the balloon with water. She would walk through the sea behind Tom so that he didn't see her coming then, suddenly, she would tip the water all over him before he had time to turn round.

Andrew Brodie: Supporting Literacy © A & C Black Publishers Ltd. 2006

The brother and sister got along very well together. Sometimes, though, they would get cross with each other.

"Don't splash me," Tom would say. "The water goes in my eyes."

"I can't help it," Kate would reply, but she knew she was making Tom cross. "Anyway, even if it does go in your eyes it won't hurt you."

One day the children were playing in the water when Tom told Kate that he had seen some sharks. Kate didn't think that Tom was telling the truth until she saw lots of white bubbles upon the top of the water.

"Quick, Tom, it's important, we must leave the water this second!" shouted Kate.

"Why?" asked Tom.

"Because you saw some sharks."

"I didn't see any really," said Tom.

"You should never lie to me," said Kate crossly.

"I was only joking."

Kate decided to keep watch because she had seen the bubbles and there might be a shark or another dangerous animal. The bubbles had gone now but something was moving in the water. Kate thought of all the animals and fish that live in the sea – which one could it be?

Suddenly a dark shape swam between Kate and Tom. They both screamed. Mum and Dad heard the screams and came running down the beach to see what was wrong. They both laughed when a lady in a wetsuit came out of the water and walked up the beach!

Notes for teachers

Dictionary card

The next four sheets of this book are designed to be photocopied back to back then laminated and joined to make a folding 'dictionary' of very useful words. The dictionary consists of all the high frequency NLS words for Reception, Year 1 and Year 2, (except for 'I', 'a', the pupils' own addresses and the address of the school) together with all the medium frequency words specified for Years 4 and 5.

In addition to these lists we have listed other words, including all those that are needed to complete the worksheets in this book and many that are likely to appear in Year 6 work in other curriculum areas.

Each child should be given a laminated copy. This will become a tremendously useful resource to be used for dictionary work and for general spelling help.

Smiley face words

The final four sheets of the book consist of 'smiley face' worksheets showing all the medium frequency words recommended for Years 4 and 5 except for following: turned, walked and walking (follow, turn and walk are all included). Alongside each word is a circle, on which a smiley face can be drawn. As each child improves, the smiley faces on his/her worksheets get more detailed.

Photocopy a set of four worksheets for each child. When the child is able to read each word he/she is allowed to draw a smile on the circle as a start to creating a 'smiley face'. When he/she is able to spell the word he/she can add the eyes. This spelling check should be repeated several times. Every time that the child is successful he/she can add other features, eg a nose, ears, hair, a hat.

Andrew Brodie: Supporting Literacy © A & C Black Publishers Ltd. 2006

Dictionary card

A

about
above
across
after
again
all
almost
along
also
always
am
an
ancient
and
animals
another
anther
any
are
armchair
around
as
ask
asked
at
atlas
atlases
Australia
autumn
away

B

baby
back
bad
bag
balanced
ball
balloon
bark
bat

batteries
battery
be
beach
because
bed
been
bees
before
began
being
below
best
better
between
big
bike
bird
birthday
blood
bloodhound
bluebell
boat
body
boil
boiling
book
born
both
boy
bread
breath
breathe
Britain
brother
brought
bulb
burned
but
by

C

cake
call
called
came
can
can't
carbon dioxide
card
care
cat
centimetre
chair
change
cheese
children
chocolate
circuit
circulation
claws
closed
clothes
clown
coast
coin
cold
come
comes
coming
computer
consumer
could
countries
country
crab
crawling
cross
crossly
cupboard
curly
cycle

D

dad
day
diagram
did
didn't
diet
different
dig
do
doctor
does
dog
don't
door
down
downstairs
during

E

each
ear
early
earth
east
England
environment
Europe
evaporate
evaporation
every
everybody
exercise
exploration
eyes

F

fair
fast
father
favourite
female

fertilisation
fertilise
few
filament
find
fireplace
first
fish
flower
fly
follow
following
football
for
found
friends
from
front
fruit

G

garden
gas
gases
germinate
germination
get
gets
girl
globe
go
goat
goes
going
goldfish
gone
good
got
great
Greece
gymnastics

H

had
hair

half
handcuffs
happy
has
have
he
head
healthy
hear
heard
heart
held
help
her
here
high
him
his
holiday
home
homework
honey
horse
house
how
hungry
hurry
hurt

I

I'm
ice
if
important
in
inside
Ireland
is
it

J

jump
jumped
just

K

keep
kept
kettle
kilogram
kilometre
kite
knew
know

L

lady
last
late
laugh
laughing
lazy
leave
leaves
left
lifeboat
light
like
likes
liquid
listen
little
live
lived
longer
look
looking
lots

loudspeaker
love
lungs

M

made
make
male
man
many
may

me
metre
might
milk
millimetre
minutes
money
months
moon
more
morning
most
mother
mountain
Mr
Mrs
much
mudguard
mug
mum
must
my

N

name
near
never
new
newspaper
next
night
no
north
Northern Ireland
nose
not
now
nowhere
number

O

o'clock
of
off
often

Andrew Brodie: Supporting Literacy © A & C Black Publishers Ltd. 2006

old
on
once
one
onion
only
opened
or
order
other
our
out
outside
ovary
over
own
oxygen

P

paper
park
past
path
Paul
peg
people
petal
place
plant
plate
play
play
policeman
pollen
pollinate
pollination
poor
predator
producer
pull
purrs
push
put

Q

quiet

R

ran
read
reading
really
red
remember
repair
replied
reproduce
reproduction
right
river
road
round
route
running

S

said
sand
saucepan
saw
say
school
Scotland
second
see
seen
series
she
sheepdog
shoes
shop
should
shouldn't
shouted
show
sister
sitting
slide
slow

small
sneeze
so
solid
some
something
sometimes
sound
south
speed
springtime
stamen
stare
started
stay
stayed
stem
stigma
still
stir
stop
stopped
storm
story
straw
strawberry
style
such
suddenly
summer
sun
sure
swimming
swings
switch

T

table
take
talking
taste
teacher
teaspoon
television
tell

than
that
the
their
them
then
there
these
they
things
think
this
those
thought
three
through
tie
time
to
today
toes
together
told
Tom
too
took
towards
toys
train
travel
tree
tries
Tudor
turn
turned
twirl
two

U

under
United Kingdom
until
up
upon
upstairs

us
used
usually

V

vapour
vegetables
very
Victorians

W

Wales
walk
walked
walking
want
war
was
watch
water
water
way
we
wear
weekend
went
were
west
what
when
where
while
white
who
whole
why
will
windmill
window
wire
with

without
woke
woken
woman
word
work
world
worm
worry
would
write

X

X-ray

Y

year
yes
you
young
your

Z

zoo

NUMBERS

one
two
three
four
five
six
seven
eight
nine
ten
eleven
twelve
thirteen
fourteen
fifteen
sixteen
seventeen
eighteen
nineteen
twenty

DAYS

Monday
Tuesday
Wednesday
Thursday
Friday
Saturday
Sunday

MONTHS

January
February
March
April
May
June
July
August
September
October
November
December

COLOURS

black
white
red
blue
green
yellow
orange
pink
brown
purple

ADDRESS WORDS

street
road
crescent
lane
avenue
city
town
village
country
school
postcode

Andrew Brodie: Supporting Literacy © A & C Black Publishers Ltd. 2006

Smiley face words

above ◯	baby ◯	brother ◯
across ◯	balloon ◯	brought ◯
almost ◯	before ◯	can't ◯
along ◯	began ◯	change ◯
also ◯	being ◯	children ◯
always ◯	below ◯	clothes ◯
animals ◯	better ◯	coming ◯
any ◯	between ◯	didn't ◯
around ◯	birthday ◯	different ◯
asked ◯	both ◯	does ◯

don't	garden	important
during	goes	inside
earth	gone	jumped
every	great	knew
eyes	half	know
father	happy	lady
first	head	leave
follow	heard	light
found	high	might
friends	I'm	money

Andrew Brodie: Supporting Literacy © A & C Black Publishers Ltd. 2006

morning ◯	outside ◯	something ◯
mother ◯	own ◯	sometimes ◯
much ◯	paper ◯	sound ◯
near ◯	place ◯	started ◯
never ◯	right ◯	still ◯
number ◯	round ◯	stopped ◯
often ◯	second ◯	such ◯
only ◯	show ◯	suddenly ◯
opened ◯	sister ◯	sure ◯
other ◯	small ◯	swimming ◯

think	until	window
those	upon	without
thought	used	woke
through	walk	woken
today	watch	word
together	where	work
told	while	world
tries	white	write
turn	whole	year
under	why	young

Andrew Brodie: Supporting Literacy © A & C Black Publishers Ltd. 2006